This Donut Date Journal
Records the Stories of:

The Disciple Making Parent's

Donut Date Journal 2
Family History Edition

70 Questions for Children
to Ask Their Parents

Chap Bettis

DIAMOND HILL
PUBLISHING

THE DISCIPLE-MAKING PARENT'S DONUT DATE JOURNAL 2:
FAMILY HISTORY EDITION - 70 Questions for Children to Ask Their Parents
Copyright © 2017 by Chap Bettis.
Diamond Hill Publishing
All rights reserved.
ISBN-13: 978-0999041024
ISBN-10: 0999041029

For more information or to order in bulk
visit www.donutdatejournal.com

A special thanks to Bella Sandoval and Savannah Gardner
for suggesting this idea to their moms!

Cover and interior design by Jeff Flynn
www.jflycreative.com

TABLE OF CONTENTS

IMPORTANT DATES

INTRODUCTION

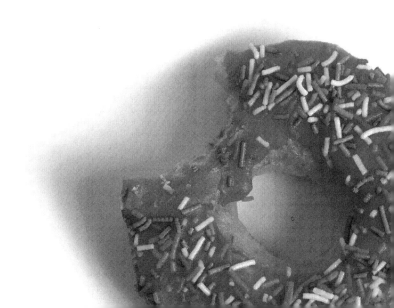

Introduction

I had just released *The Disciple-Making Parent's Donut Date Journal* and it was doing quite well. I was excited about happy parents who were loving this time with their children. Then within one day of each other, I had similar requests. Two different young people each asked their parents:

"Where is my journal to ask you questions?"

These parents contacted me and essentially said the same thing, "We love *The Donut Date Journal*. But could you please make one for children to ask questions of their parents?"

"Of course!" I thought to myself. "Why didn't I think of that before? What a great way for children to show honor to their parents—by learning their parents' stories!"

As I reflected more, I realized how valuable something like this would be for me. I have heard stories from my parents. But those stories had come in bits and pieces throughout the years. Over time the details have begun to fade. In addition, because I heard the stories piecemeal, I don't remember the chronology or specific years.

But I do want to remember. This is my heritage. These are people I love!

After some work, I am a delighted to release *The Donut Date Journal 2: Family History Edition*. In this companion journal you will find 70 questions for children to ask their parents.

I think young children will enjoy asking these questions. At this age, they are eager to hear their parents' stories and will find them interesting.

Even more, teens and adult children will enjoy asking their parents these questions. Although it has Donut Date in the title, this journal could make for stimulating conversation around the holiday table or on a long car trip. And for teens, this resource can help them connect with their parents and grandparents.

God commands his people to show honor to their parents and the aged. Unfortunately we live in a time when families are often child-centered. This resource can help bind families together and honor the different generations.

I offer it to you in the hope that it deepens the love and respect in your family!

QUESTIONS AND ANSWERS

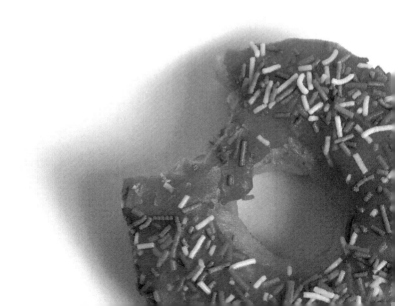

Tell me about your grandparents. What do you remember?

What is some of the earliest family history you were told by a parent or grandparent?

Where were your mom and dad born? How did they meet?

_____

_____

_____

_____

_____

_____

_____

_____

_____

_____

_____

_____

_____

_____

_____

_____

_____

_____

_____

What did your dad do for work? Where? What years?

What did your mom do for work? Where? What years?

What was your mom like?
List at least five words that describe her.

What was your dad like?
List at least five words that describe him.

Do you remember any big family events that have funny stories?

What else about our family history do you think I should know?

What did you do for elementary school? What do you remember about those years?

What did you do for junior high? What do you remember about those years?

What did you do for high school? What do you remember about those years?

What were you like in high school?

What were your favorite subjects in school? Why?

Who were your favorite teachers?
What did you like about them?

What kinds of car/transportation did you have?

Did you have any big disagreements with your parents growing up? What were they about?

What was your favorite birthday memory growing up?

What are some of your favorite vacation memories?

What are some of your favorite Christmas memories?

What were some of your favorite toys?

Did you have any family traditions for Christmas, vacation, or birthdays? Which ones do you remember best?

Did you have any pets? Why or why not? What were their names? What do you remember about them?

What were your favorite board games?

What were some of your favorite books?

What activities (sports or extra-curricular) did you do? What do you remember about those?

_____

_____

_____

_____

_____

_____

_____

_____

_____

_____

_____

_____

_____

_____

_____

_____

_____

_____

_____

_____

_____

What are some of your favorite foods?
What foods do you not like? What are some
foods you were served when you were sick?

What were your summer jobs?
What years did you do them?
What do you remember about those?

_____

_____

_____

_____

_____

_____

_____

_____

_____

_____

_____

_____

_____

_____

_____

_____

_____

_____

_____

_____

Where did you live as a child or teen?
What do you remember?

What memories do you have about your brothers and sisters?

What do you love most about your brothers and sisters?

_____

_____

_____

_____

_____

_____

_____

_____

_____

_____

_____

_____

_____

_____

_____

_____

_____

_____

_____

Who were some of your best friends?
What did you like about them?

_____

_____

_____

_____

_____

_____

_____

_____

_____

_____

_____

_____

_____

_____

_____

_____

_____

_____

_____

Who were your favorite musicians? Actors/actresses? Sports stars?

Were there any fads that you participated in when you were young?

What schools or military service did you complete after high school?

What is your favorite time of year? Why?

When did you become a Christian? How?

What was church like growing up?

What do you remember about Vacation Bible School, youth meetings, or Sunday School?

What were some of your favorite Bible verses?

What are some of the big events or answers to prayer that built your faith?

How have you seen God at work recently?

_____

_____

_____

_____

_____

_____

_____

_____

_____

_____

_____

_____

_____

_____

_____

_____

_____

_____

_____

_____

Who are some people you admire in our church? Why?

What are some things that you think few people understand about you?

What are some hard lessons you have learned that I need to know about?

What makes you unique?
Describe yourself in five words (or more).

What big events in our country or world history do you remember?
What do you remember about those times?

_____

_____

_____

_____

_____

_____

_____

_____

_____

_____

_____

_____

_____

_____

_____

_____

_____

_____

_____

_____

_____

What do you think young people need to know that they don't know?

_____

_____

_____

_____

_____

_____

_____

_____

_____

_____

_____

_____

_____

_____

_____

_____

_____

_____

_____

_____

How did you meet Dad/Mom?

When did you know you wanted to marry Dad/Mom?

_____

_____

_____

_____

_____

_____

_____

_____

_____

_____

_____

_____

_____

_____

_____

_____

_____

_____

_____

_____

What funny stories do you have about Dad/Mom?

What do you remember most about your wedding day?

What do you remember most about your honeymoon?

What do you remember about that first year of marriage?

What advice would you give to your children/grandchildren on their wedding day?

_____

_____

_____

_____

_____

_____

_____

_____

_____

_____

_____

_____

_____

_____

_____

_____

_____

_____

_____

_____

What were your full-time jobs? What years? What do you remember from those? What life lessons did you learn in those?

Tell me the story of the day I was born.

_____

_____

_____

_____

_____

_____

_____

_____

_____

_____

_____

_____

_____

_____

_____

_____

_____

_____

Where did you live when I was born and after? What do you remember about those years?

What were some rewarding things about raising kids?

What is (was) the hardest part about raising me?

What are some of the most amazing places you have been?

_____

_____

_____

_____

_____

_____

_____

_____

_____

_____

_____

_____

_____

_____

_____

_____

_____

_____

_____

What were the best years of your life so far?

What are some things you have done that you are really proud of?

_____

_____

_____

_____

_____

_____

_____

_____

_____

_____

_____

_____

_____

_____

_____

_____

_____

_____

_____

Other than your family, who have been some of the most important people in your life? Why?

_____

_____

_____

_____

_____

_____

_____

_____

_____

_____

_____

_____

_____

_____

_____

_____

_____

_____

_____

_____

What would I be surprised to learn about you?

What were some hard decisions you had to make?

If you could do anything over in
your life, what would it be?
How would you do it differently?

What were some important spiritual lessons you would like to pass on to your children/grandchildren?

What other life lessons have you learned that you want to pass on to me?

_____

_____

_____

_____

_____

_____

_____

_____

_____

_____

_____

_____

_____

_____

_____

_____

_____

_____

_____

_____

What are some times you have seen God move that increased your faith in him?

Write your own question here.

Write your own question here.

Write your own question here.

Write your own question here.

_____

_____

_____

_____

_____

_____

_____

_____

_____

_____

_____

_____

_____

_____

_____

_____

_____

_____

_____

_____

Write your own question here.

_____

_____

_____

_____

_____

_____

_____

_____

_____

_____

_____

_____

_____

_____

_____

_____

_____

_____

_____

_____

Write your own question here.

_____

_____

_____

_____

_____

_____

_____

_____

_____

_____

_____

_____

_____

_____

_____

_____

_____

_____

_____

Write your own question here.

_____
_____
_____
_____
_____
_____
_____
_____
_____
_____
_____
_____
_____
_____
_____
_____
_____
_____
_____
_____
_____
_____
_____

Write your own question here.

Important Dates

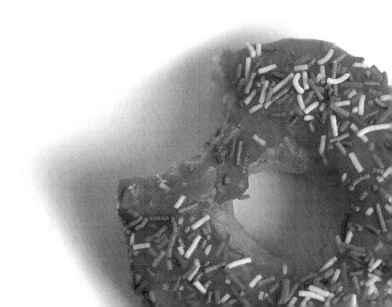

A Year-by-Year Overview

Use these pages to record an overview of important dates and events at a glance. List the years along with the events.

_____

_____

_____

_____

_____

_____

_____

_____

_____

_____

_____

_____

_____

_____

_____

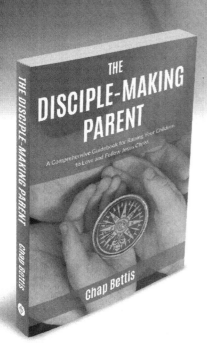

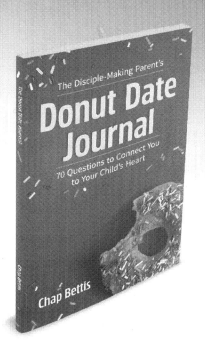